Charles Peattie and Mark Warren

Masterley Publishing

Celeb

First published in 2002 by
MASTERLEY PUBLISHING

Design and digital artwork by
OCEAN Digital Media.com

These cartoons first appeared in Private Eye between 1987 and 2002

With thanks to:

Ian Hislop for first "discovering" Gary,
Russell Taylor for additional material,
and Harry Enfield for being a great Bloke.

GARY, FOR YOUR THIRD RECORD YOU'VE CHOSEN 'FEED THE WORLD' BY BAND AID, WHY?

WELL MICHAEL, I REALLY LIKE THE MELODY AND I REALLY LIKE THE LYRIC. I PLAY IT A LOT...

IT'S GOT A MESSAGE FOR ALL OF US. WHENEVER I'M IN A RESTAURANT I JUST WHISTLE THE TUNE IN MY HEAD...

AND I THINK, GARY, NO SECONDS FOR YOU, YOU'VE HAD ENOUGH.

SITTING BY THE POOL IN HOLLYWOOD IS ALL VERY WELL, BUT IT'S A BIT ARTIFICIAL...

WHAT I REALLY LIKE TO DO ON A DAY LIKE THIS IS WANDER OUT AND PLAY SOME CRICKET WITH THE VILLAGE TEAM...

SO I'M HAVING THEM ALL FLOWN OUT HERE...

SECOND CLASS. YOU KNOW, NOTHING FLASH.

DON'T GET ME WRONG... I LOVE ENGLAND. YOU WON'T FIND ANYONE MORE PATRIOTIC THAN ME.

BEST COUNTRY IN THE WORLD.

BUT WHEN YOUR ACCOUNTANT TELLS YOU THAT FOR EVERY POUND YOU'RE EARNING, THE TAXMAN'S TAKING TWO...

YOU'VE GOT TO SACK HIM AND GET ONE OF THESE WISED UP HARVARD BOYS...

WELL YES I SUPPOSE I DO HAVE A SWIMMING POOL...

BUT I'M NOT LIKE THESE HOLLYWOOD SHOW-OFFS...

I DON'T REALLY CARE ABOUT THAT SORT OF THING. I JUST TREAT IT ALL AS A JOKE...

I DROVE MY ROLLS INTO IT LAST WEEK...

11

Here, listen to this :— "Another celebrity client, Gary Bloke, was seen entering the exclusive massage club, midday on Tuesday..."

"... He left 15 minutes later by the front door. His car brazenly parked outside..." Bloody liars!

They make it up as they go along. I find it very hurtful.

I was in there for a good hour and a half. Chantelle was quite exhausted.

Bastards!

Beluga caviare? No thanks mate.

You sure?

Positive. I used to quite like it, as it happens, but then I found out where it comes from.

What, Russia?

Nah. Fishes' bottoms.

Only joking. Gissa dollop.

I know I'm not supposed to say anything political but I just want to send this message of goodwill...

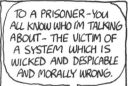

To a prisoner—you all know who I'm talking about— the victim of a system which is wicked and despicable and morally wrong.

They've locked him away. They've taken away his liberty... and now they've taken away the one thing he values above all else...

His O.B.E.

Lester Piggot. Here's to you mate. Victim of the most vicious and draconian taxation system the world has ever...

Er...

Tap Tap

My birthday party at Stringfellows? Smashing little bash that was. Best ever.

Nothing too glitzy mind. None of this showgirls jumping out of cakes malarkey I think that's poncey.

Not your style, Gary.

Nah. You'll never guess what Peter laid on instead.

What?

He had them jump out from this immense shepherds pie. Three of them there was. Sisters.

Oh that's nice

Very tasty.

12

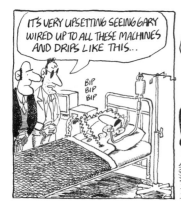

55

RIGHT, I'M OFF TO THE T.V. STUDIO TO DO MY BIT FOR COMIC RELIEF.

GOOD FOR YOU, GARY.

IT'S GOING TO BE A REAL CHARITY MARATHON THIS YEAR. DOESN'T FINISH UNTIL 3 IN THE MORNING.

CRIKEY. YOU'LL BE SHATTERED, MATE.

BEFORE YOU GO: "DON'T FORGET YOUR NOSE."

NO NEED. THERE'LL BE PLENTY THERE AT THE STUDIO FOR US TO USE, I'M SURE.

BETTER TAKE THIS STUPID LITTLE THING TO WEAR THOUGH I SUPPOSE.

WELL I WARNED HIM YEARS AGO ABOUT THE DANGERS OF GETTING TOO INVOLVED IN THE DEMON WHITE POWDER BUT HE WOULDN'T LISTEN...

I MEAN LOTS OF US CELEBRITIES GET TEMPTED. IT'S THE LIFESTYLE ISN'T IT? BUT WHEN YOU'RE OFFERED IT, IF YOU'RE SMART YOU JUST SAY NO.

COULD'VE DESTROYED HIS CAREER, THAT STUFF, YOU KNOW...

I'M JUST GLAD HE'S PULLED HIMSELF TOGETHER AND DECIDED TO PACK IT IN... AS A HIGH PROFILE FIGURE HE WAS BECOMING AN EMBARRASSMENT.

YOU CAN SAY THAT AGAIN...

ABOUT AS STREET CRED AS FAIRY LIQUID.

SHOWBIZ NEWS
DANNY BAKER TO QUIT DAZ COMMERCIALS

7, 15, 22... OH DEAR! DAMN..

EVERY SUNDAY MORNING HE GOES THROUGH THE SAME SILLY RITUAL TO SEE IF HE'S BEEN LUCKY OR NOT.

BLAST.

IT'S PATHETIC IF YOU ASK ME.

A PERSON OF GARY'S WEALTH CHECKING IF HE'S WON THE NATIONAL LOTTERY?

NO. GARY TOTTING UP THE COLUMN INCHES HE'S GOT IN THE TABLOIDS AND SUPPLEMENTS.

OH WELL. BETTER LUCK NEXT WEEK.

ROD, YOU TARTAN TERROR! YOU ANNOUNCE YOU'RE RETIRING FROM SHOWBIZ ON THE SUNDAY THEN ON THE MONDAY YOU SAY IT WAS ALL A MISTAKE.

I'D HAD A FEW BEVVIES TOO MANY, GARY. I DIDN'T KNOW WHAT I WAS SAYING...

PEOPLE ARE NOW SUGGESTING IT WAS JUST A CHEAP PUBLICITY TRICK TO SELL TICKETS FOR YOUR WORLD TOUR.

NOTHING COULD BE FURTHER FROM THE TRUTH, MATE.

MY PR CHARGED ME A FORTUNE FOR THINKING UP THAT STUNT.

LET'S JUST HOPE IT WORKS, EH?

I TRIED TO PUT UP A FRONT BUT BASICALLY I COULDN'T COPE...THERE WAS SOMETHING I WAS ALWAYS BLOCKING OUT...

I WAS HAVING TO DEAL WITH ALL THESE DIFFERENT PRESSURES.. I DIDN'T KNOW WHICH WAY TO TURN...

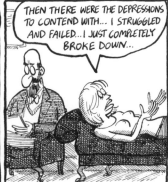

THEN THERE WERE THE DEPRESSIONS TO CONTEND WITH... I STRUGGLED AND FAILED... I JUST COMPLETELY BROKE DOWN...

SO YOU MESSED UP YOUR AUDITION AS A WEATHER GIRL THEN?

YES. BIG TIME I'M AFRAID. I WAS USELESS...

LIKE MOST DINERS IN L.A. ALL THE WAITRESSES HERE ARE RESTING MODELS OR ACTRESSES WAITING TO BE DISCOVERED.

YEAH?

YOU CAN TELL BY THE WAY THEY WALK AND HOW THEY CARRY THEMSELVES.

CAN I GET YOU ANYTHING ELSE?

JUST MORE SUGAR IN THE COFFEE.. GIVE US ANOTHER SACHET WILL YOU, DOLL?

SURE THING MR BLOKE.

I'D SASHAY MY BUTT OFF FOR YOU.

WIGGLE SLINK

SEE WHAT I MEAN?!

WHAT WERE YOU ON AT THAT CLUB LAST NIGHT? ONE MINUTE YOU WERE FINE, THE NEXT YOU SEEMED OUT OF YOUR HEAD...

I KNOW, BARRY.

YOU WERE CRAWLING AROUND ON YOUR HANDS AND KNEES SCREAMING YOU COULDN'T SEE... IT WAS SCARY, GARY.

FREAKED ME OUT AS WELL, MATE...

I'D DRUNK QUITE A LOT... THEN I DROPPED A TAB OF ACID... SILLY I. KNOW.

YOU IDIOT, GARY.'

I HAD TO PRETEND I'D LOST A CONTACT LENS.. IT TOOK ME HALF AN HOUR TO FIND IT.

WHAT ON EARTH'S HAPPENED TO PIXIE FROU FROU, GARY? SHE LOOKS LIKE A BAG OF BONES.

SHE'S AT THAT AGE, MATE HASN'T EATEN PROPERLY FOR MONTHS.

BUT SHE'S A WALKING SKELETON. WHAT YOU GOING TO DO?

DEBS TOOK HER TO HAVE SOME TESTS DONE YESTERDAY.

AND?

THEY CONFIRMED OUR WORST SUSPICIONS. IT'S SUCH A TRAGIC WASTE.

THEY SAY SHE'S STILL TOO YOUNG TO BE A MODEL.

WHAT?! SHE'S PRACTICALLY THIRTEEN.

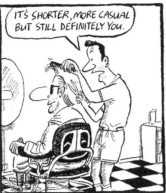

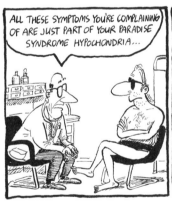

Also from Masterley Publishing

The Best of Alex 2002
By Charles Peattie & Russell Taylor

The BEST OF ALEX 2002 is the latest installment in the corporate adventures of ALEX the pinstriped cartoon character who appears daily on the business pages of the DAILY TELEGRAPH.

It's been the toughest year so far in Alex's fifteen year career. The financial world is rocked by scandals (Enron, WorldCom) and the unread small print about shares going down as well as up has come into force with a vengeance. Alex's usual concerns about maximising his Christmas bonus go out of the window as he has to fight a rearguard action to ensure that his name is not included on the regular lists of headcount reductions that are sweeping Megabank, the global investment bank where he is employed.

£9.99 (plus p&p)

Cartoon Originals and Prints

The Celeb and Alex cartoon strip originals are all for sale. A strip measures 4x14 inches. If there's a particular one you want, phone or email us some information about it (the date it appeared, what the punch line was etc.) and we'll let you know if we still have it. If the original is not available, or you are too mean to purchase it, we can make a print of it for you. Originals and prints are signed by the creators.

For further details on details on prices and delivery please call 01371 831846.

Originals, prints and books are available from:

Alex
Orchard End,
Watling Lane
Thaxted
CM6 2QY

Tel. 01371 831846
Fax. 01371 831847
Email alex-cartoon@etgate.co.uk

WWW.ALEXCARTOON.COM